Think, Draw, Create!

This edition published by Parragon Books Ltd in 2014
and distributed by

Parragon Inc.
440 Park Avenue South, 13th Floor
New York, NY 10016
www.parragon.com

Copyright © Parragon Books Ltd 2014

Written by Frances Prior-Reeves
Designed by Talking Design
Illustrations by Eleanor Carter

ISBN 978-1-4723-6793-8

Printed in China

Think, Draw, Create!

PaRragon

Bath · New York · Cologne · Melbourne · Delhi
Hong Kong · Shenzhen · Singapore · Amsterdam

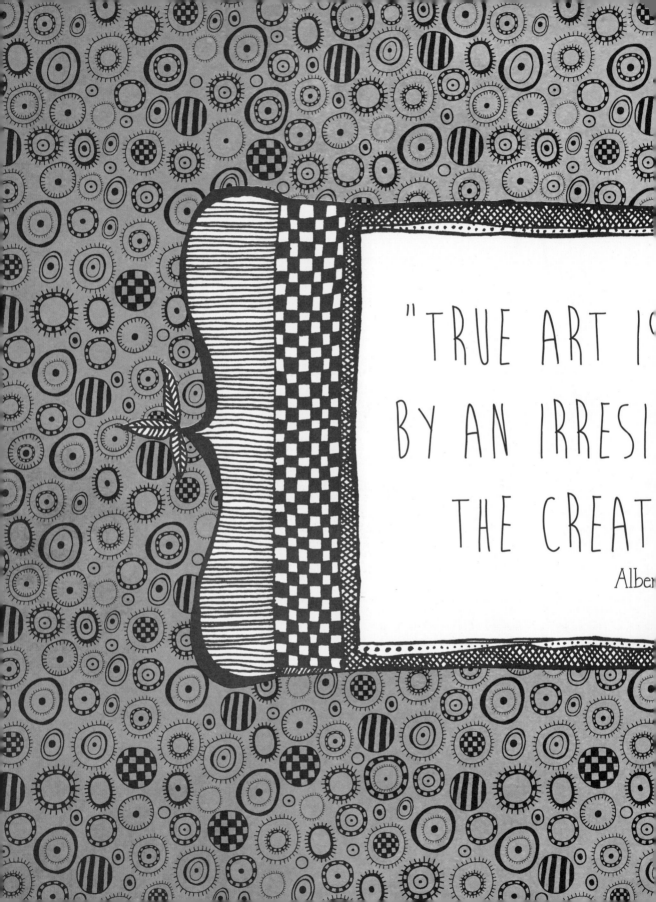

"TRUE ART I°
BY AN IRRESI
THE CREAT
Alber

HARACTERIZED
TIBLE URGE IN
E ARTIST."

Einstein

Draw the future in this
crystal ball.

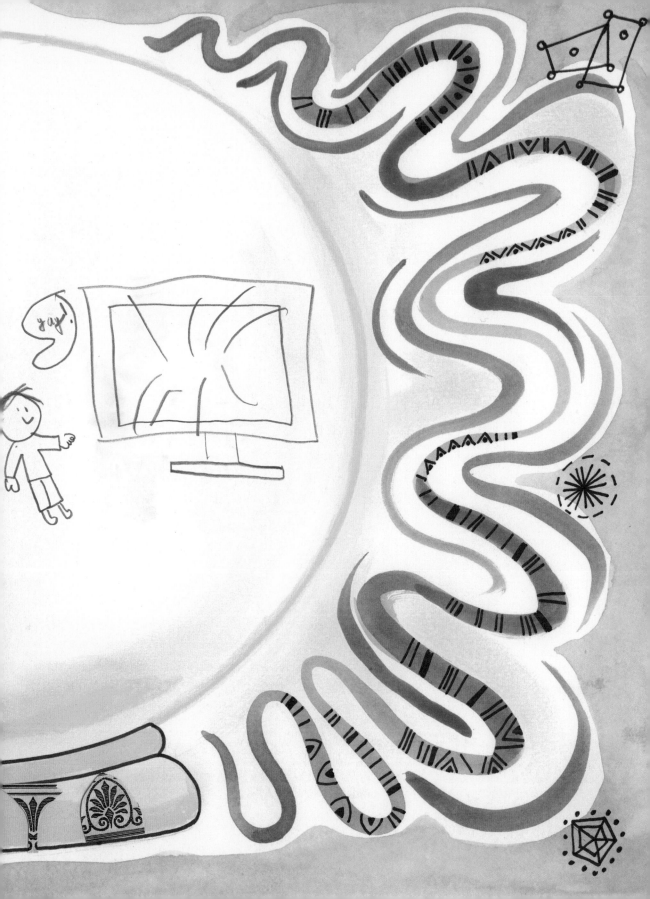

Draw this
frog's croak.

Draw something **hot.**

Draw something cold.

Unlock *this box.*

Draw what is **INSIDE**.

SPACE TO DO ANYTHING.

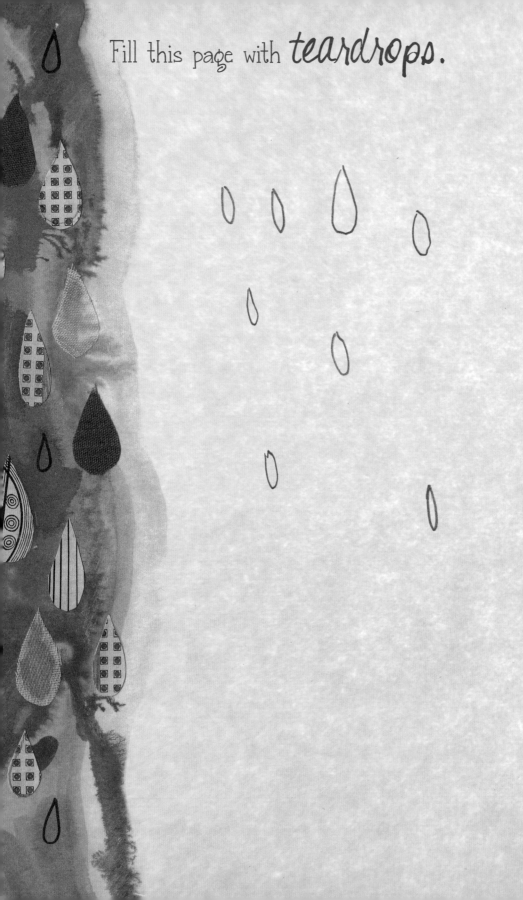

Fill this page with *teardrops.*

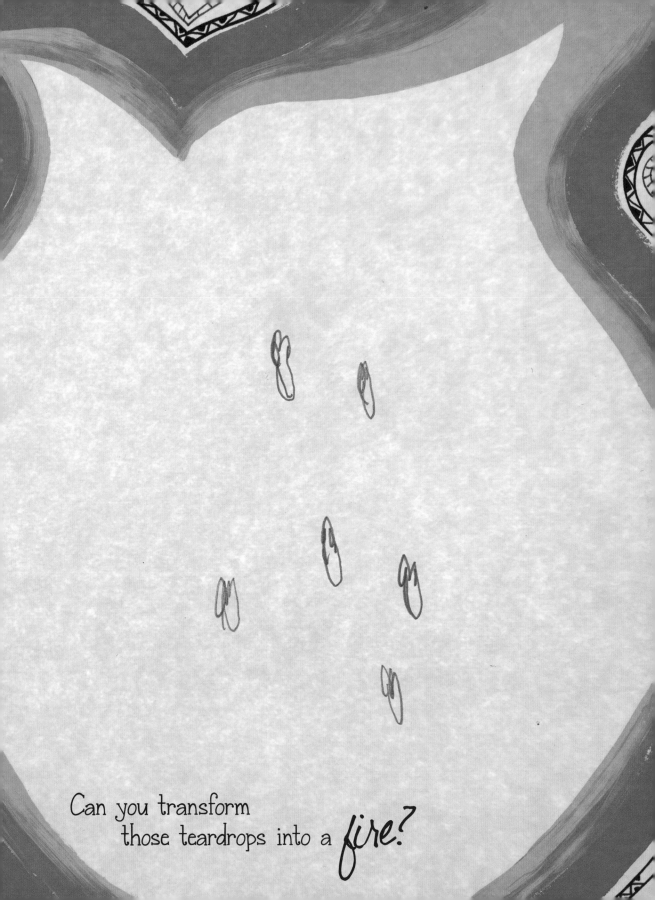

Can you transform
those teardrops into a *fire?*

Fill this pattern with as much color as possible.

Add flames to these candles.

Draw a **timeline** of your day.

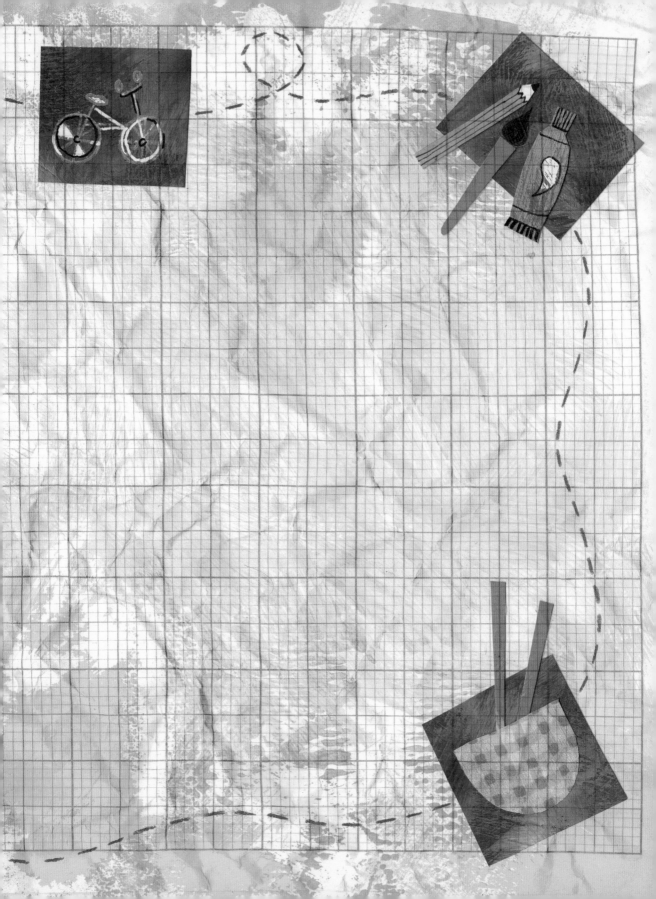

Draw what comes out at *night.*

Draw a self-portrait in a **pop-art style.**

Draw a self-portrait in an ABSTRACT STYLE.

Draw ORANGE
ignoring red.

Draw *blue* submerged
in yellow.

Draw **black**

flirting with gray.

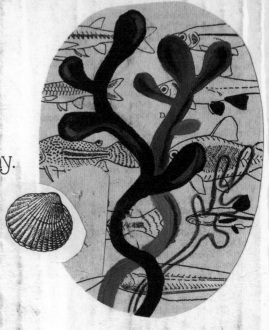

Draw the **sound**
coming from this loudspeaker.

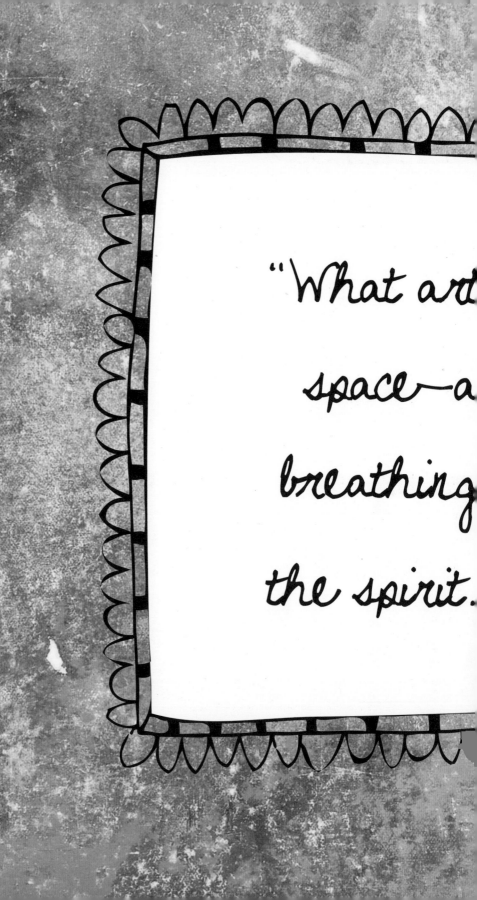

"What art[...]
space—a[...]
breathing[...]
the spirit.

offers is

certain

room for

John Updike

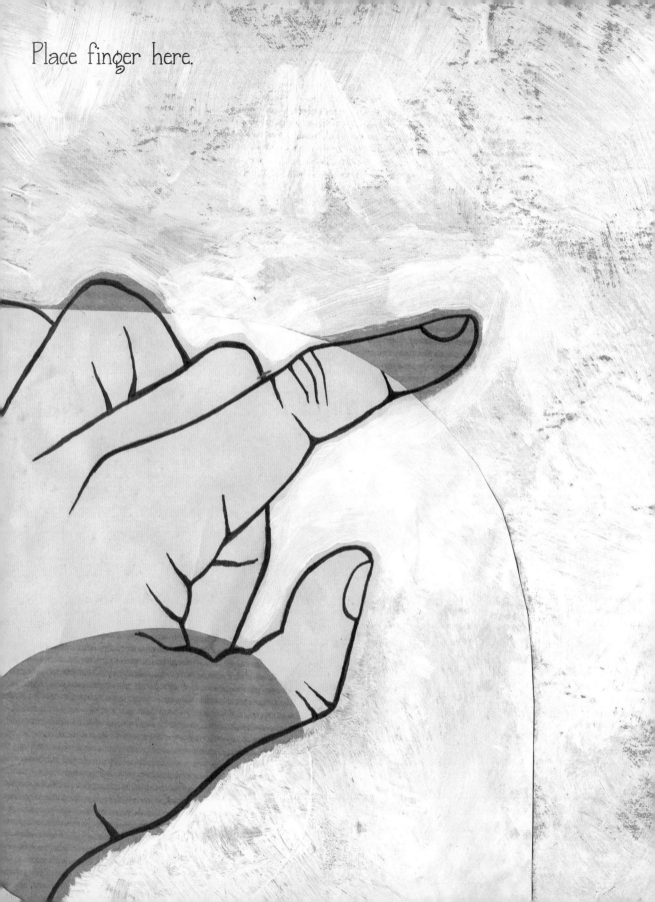
Place finger here.

Now draw something BITING it.

DON'T RESTRICT YOURSELF.

Draw your **favorite movie.**

Penquens of Madigasga

Draw your *least favorite movie.*

Draw your **INVENTION**.

Razor-Gum

create

MAKE

PRACTICE

do

draw

PAINT

sketch

FIND

inspire

COPY

Draw a *bear* that is late.

Draw a TREE.

Draw the same tree but far away on this *hilltop*.

Add people under these umbrellas.

Draw your
daydream.

Using this graph paper, design a pattern
using colors that gradually get brighter.

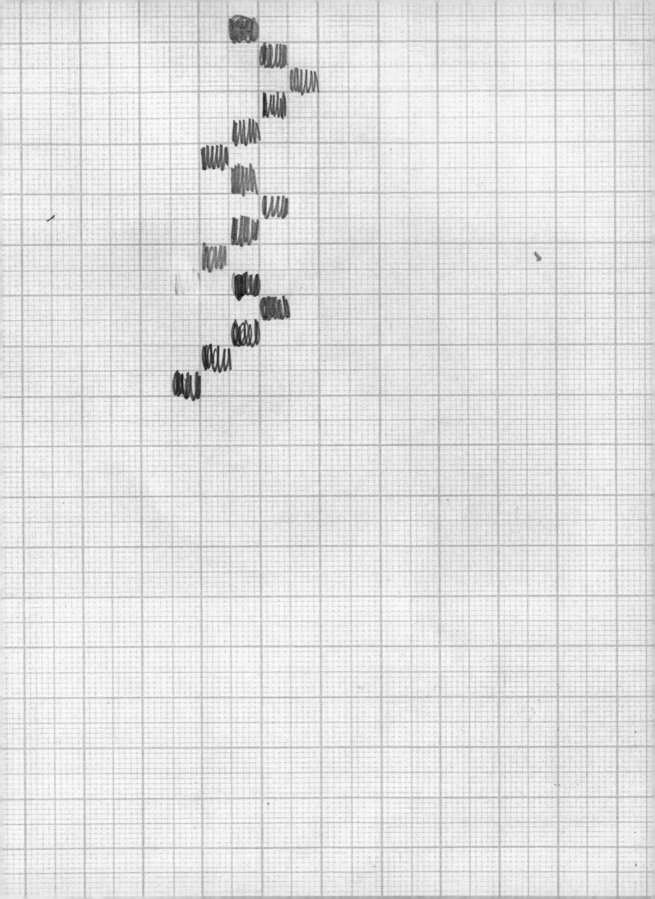

Draw hands making
shadow puppets.

Draw the view from your window in
BLACK AND WHITE.

Now draw the same view
using color,
but no outlines.

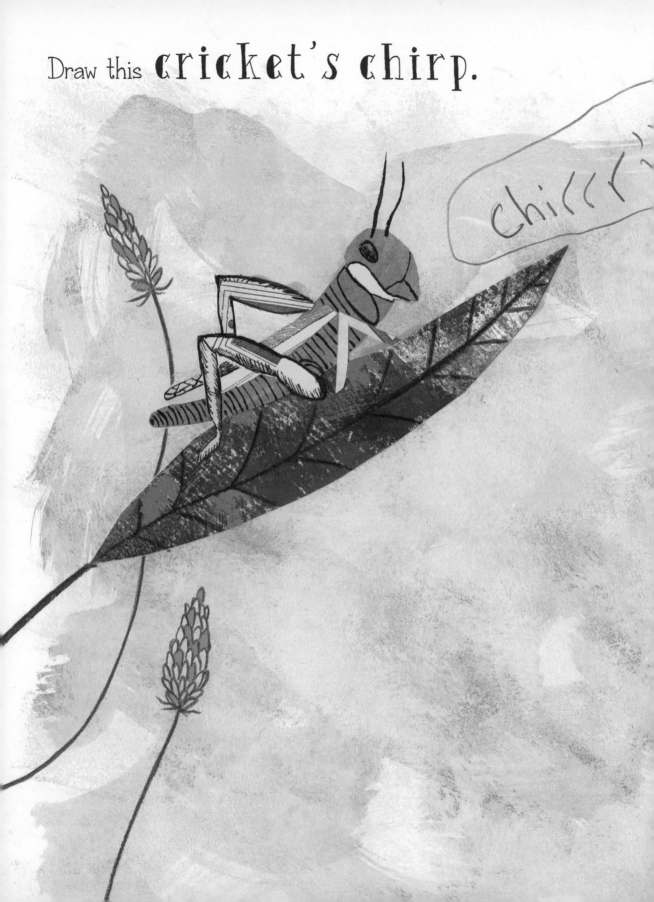

Add BODIES to these arms.

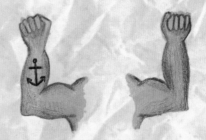

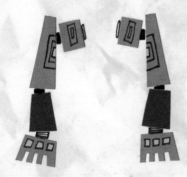

DON'T THINK,
JUST CREATE!

Draw something CURVY.

Draw the same thing using only
STRAIGHT LINES.

Design a book cover for a **SPY NOVEL.**

SPY

KidS

The tale of Desproa

Design a book cover for a *fairy tale*.

Draw a creature

that is made up of your three favorite animals.

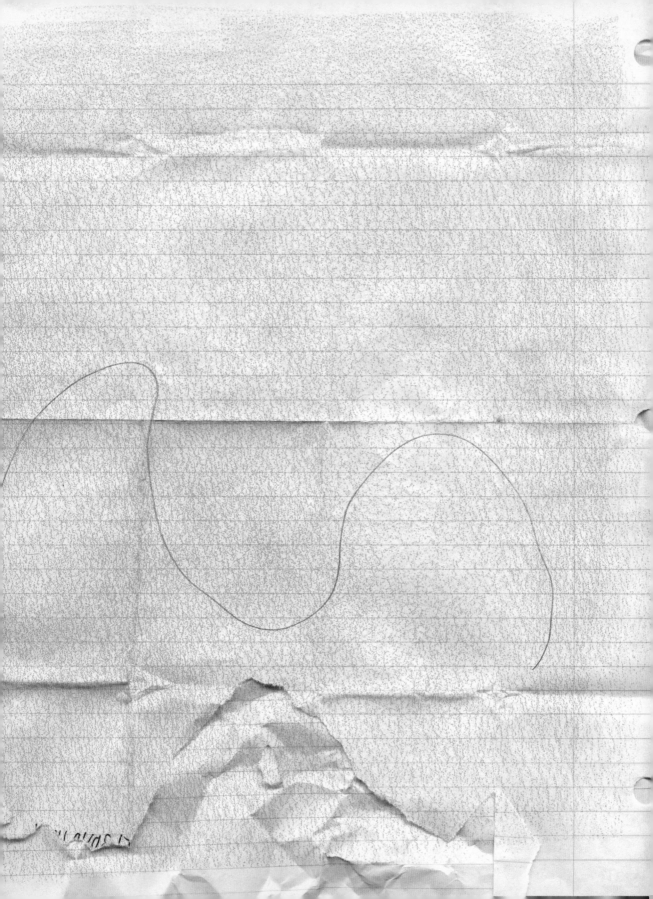

Draw a WISH.

Draw something *young*.

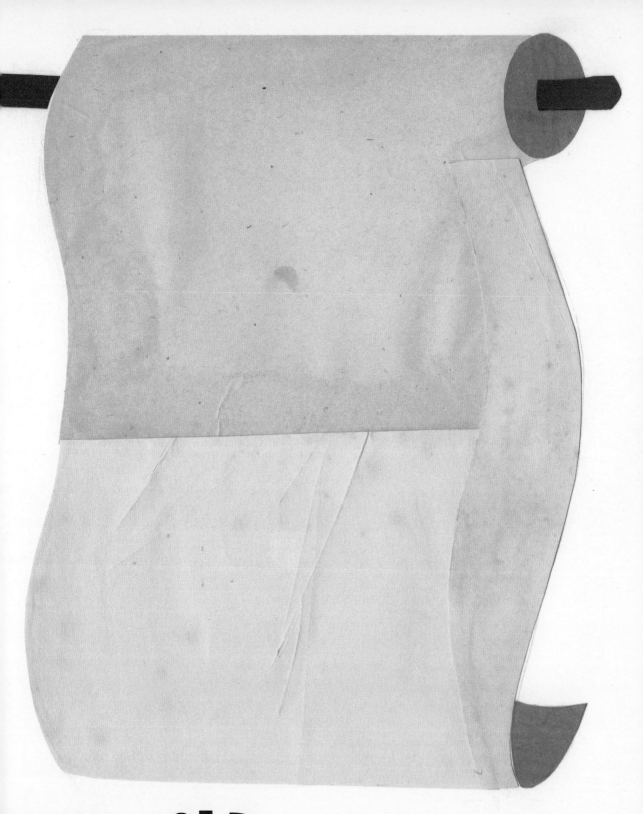

Draw something OLD.

Draw something **melting.**

"By striving to do

man has always achieved what

cautiously done no more than

never taken a single

Mikhail

the impossible,
is possible. Those who have
they believed possible have

step forward."

Bakunin

Draw cream *cursing brown.*

Draw green ADMiRING TEAL.

Draw purple

confronting
pink.

Draw a **FLYING PANDA.**

Draw a
huggable lizard.

Draw a **joke**.

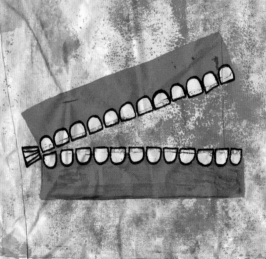

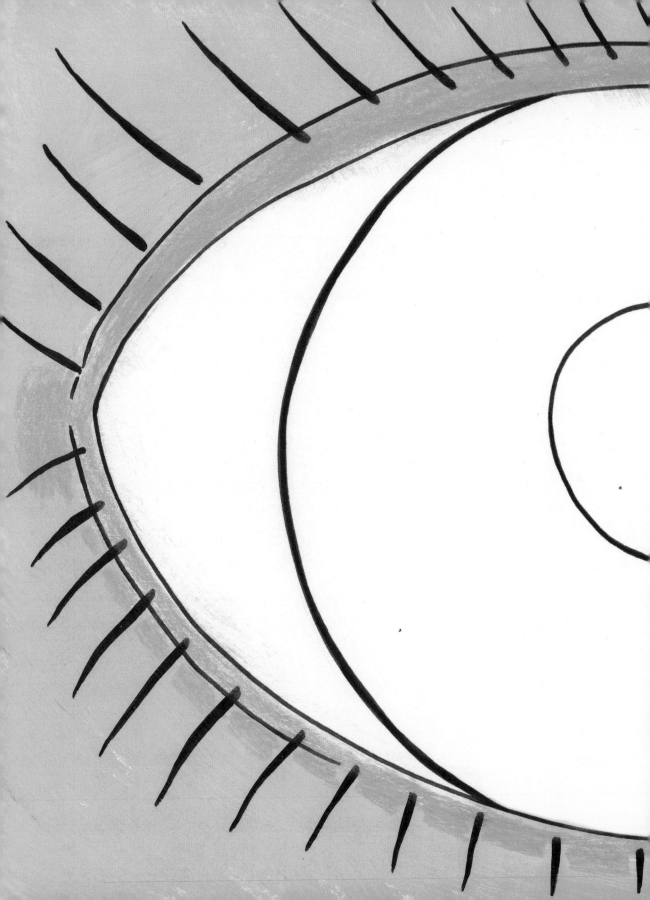

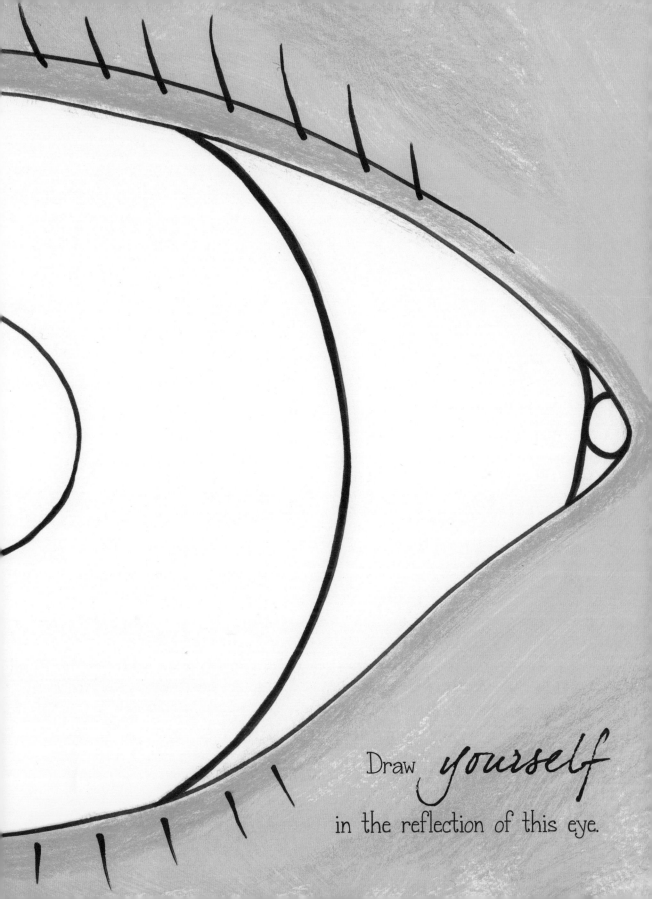

Draw *yourself* in the reflection of this eye.

Using this graph paper,
create a **MAP TO YOUR**
TREASURE.

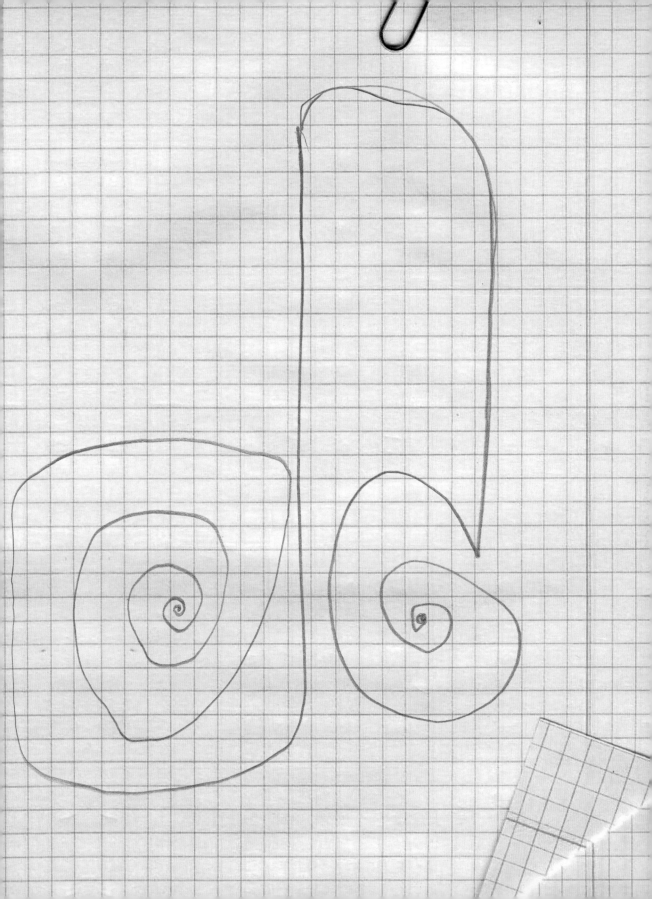

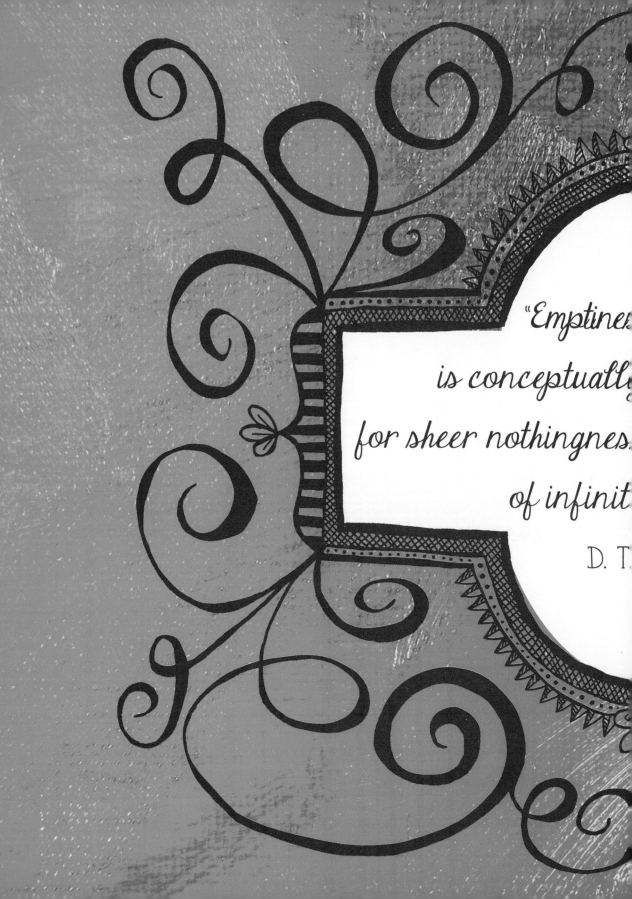

"Emptines
is conceptuall
for sheer nothingnes.
of infinit
D. T.

which

iable to be mistaken

is in fact the reservoir

possibilities."

Suzuki

Transform the emptiness.

DESIGN
ANYTHING!

Draw a **snowball fight.**

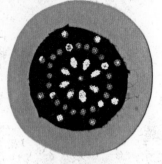

Draw something you want **right now**.

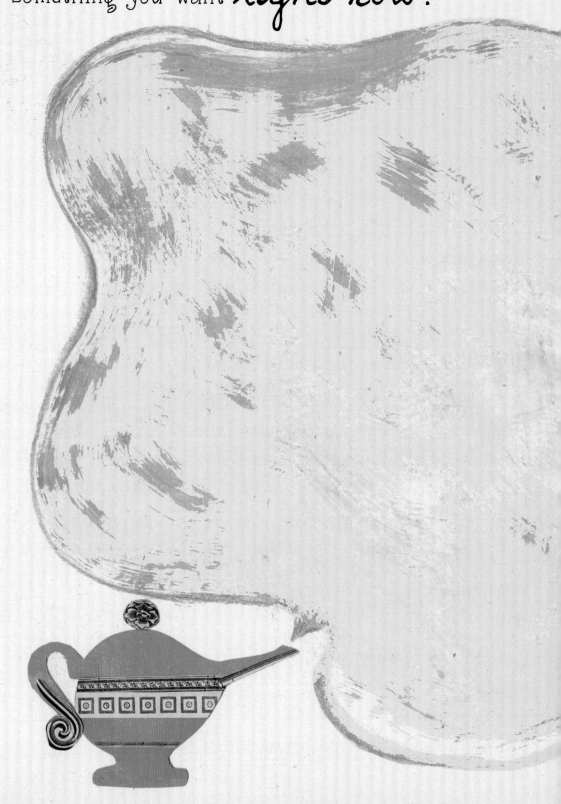

Watermelon

Draw things flying
that usually can't.

PICK UP
A PENCIL.

Fill these pages with
green creatures

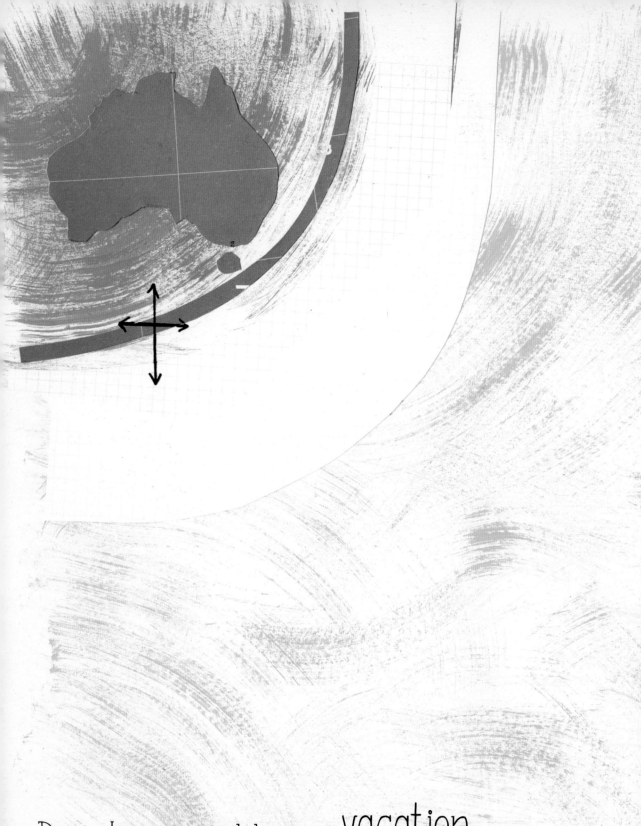

Draw where you want to go on vacation.

Draw **HEAVY** things.

Draw LIGHT things.

Fill this page with as many *different colors* as you can.

"THE CHIEF
FUNCTION
OF COLOR
SHOULD
BE TO SERVE
EXPRESSION."

Henri Matisse

Draw this *wolf's howl.*

Draw yourself angry.

Draw yourself **scared**.

possibilities

POSSIBILITIES

possibilities

possibilies

POSSIBILITIES

POSSIBILITIES

possibilities

POSSIBILITIES

possibilities

possibilities

POSSIBILITIES

possibilities

possibilities

Draw what is outside without taking your

PENCIL OFF THE PAGE.

Draw a *spider* climbing a mountain.

SHADE ANYTHING!

Draw a food chain.

Draw someone you
WANT TO MEET.

Draw your *favorite* **place.**

Draw your **least** *favorite* **place.**

Draw a **cat** trying to catch a *fish*.

INSPIRATION IS EVERYWHERE.

Draw a *rainbow* in this night sky.

Shade this pattern using a single color.

Fill this page with **X**s.

Can you transform those Xs into *birds?*

Add BODIES to these tails.

Look around you and draw
everything that is *yellow*.

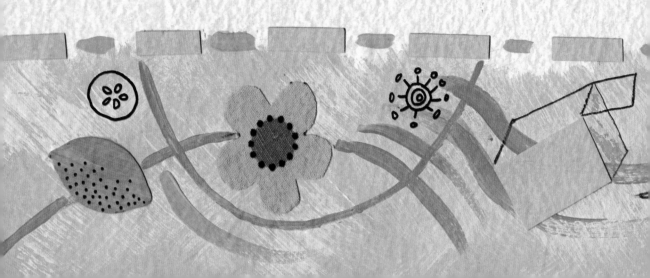

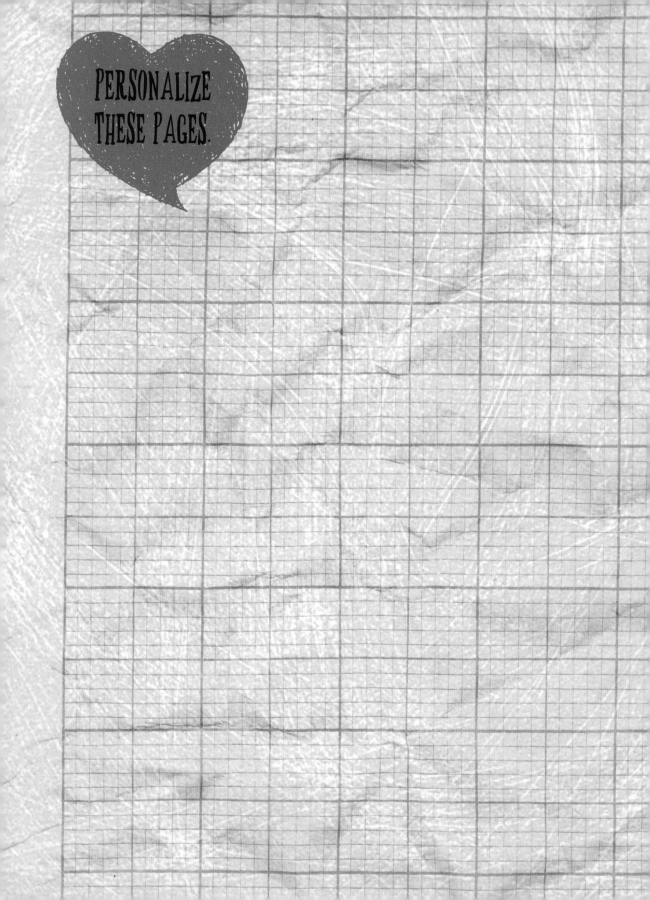

PERSONALIZE
THESE PAGES.

Draw your favorite **quotation.**

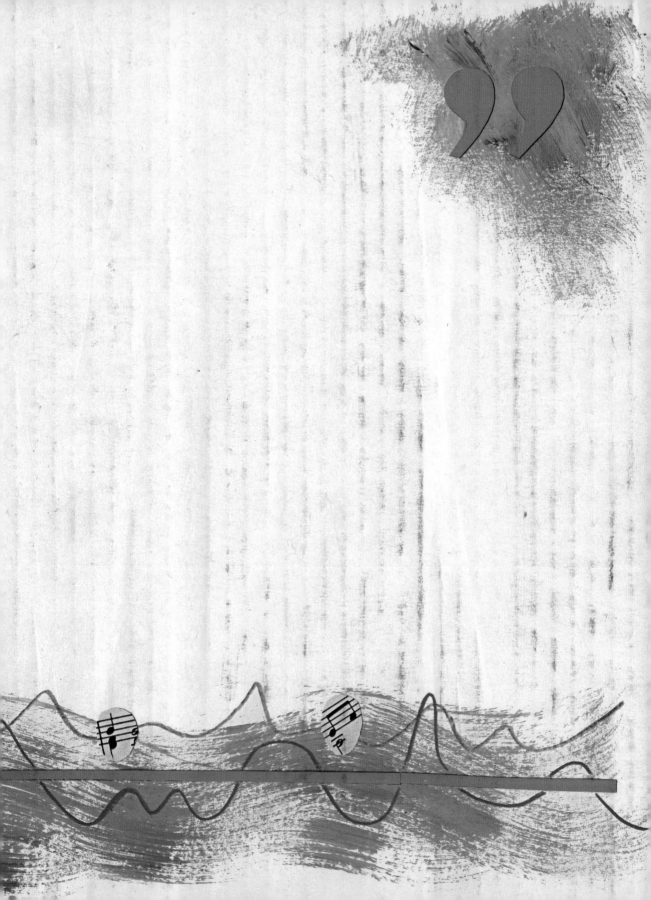

Draw what is under this
magnifying glass.

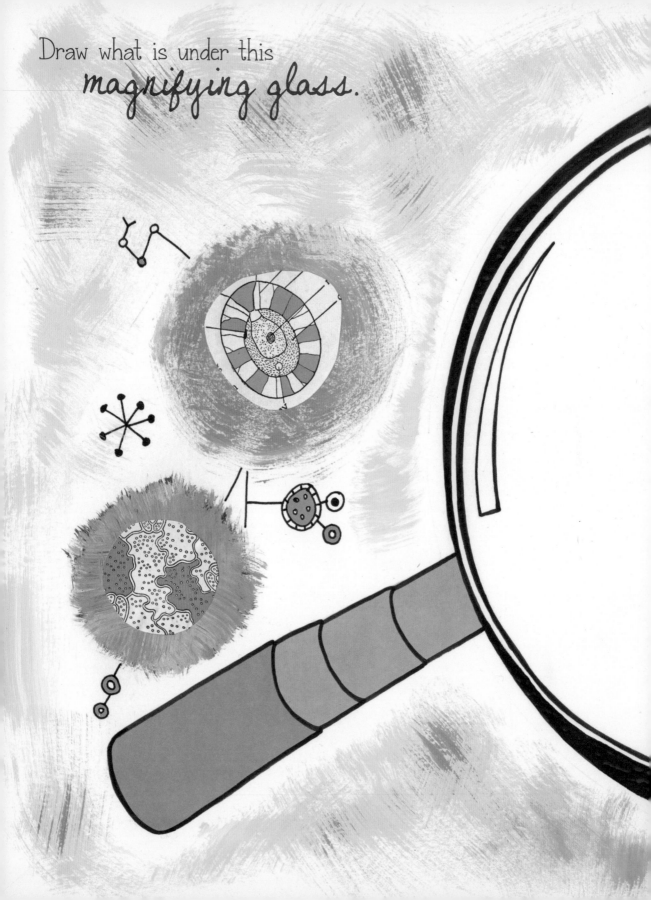

Draw something BRAVE.

Draw something
cowardly.

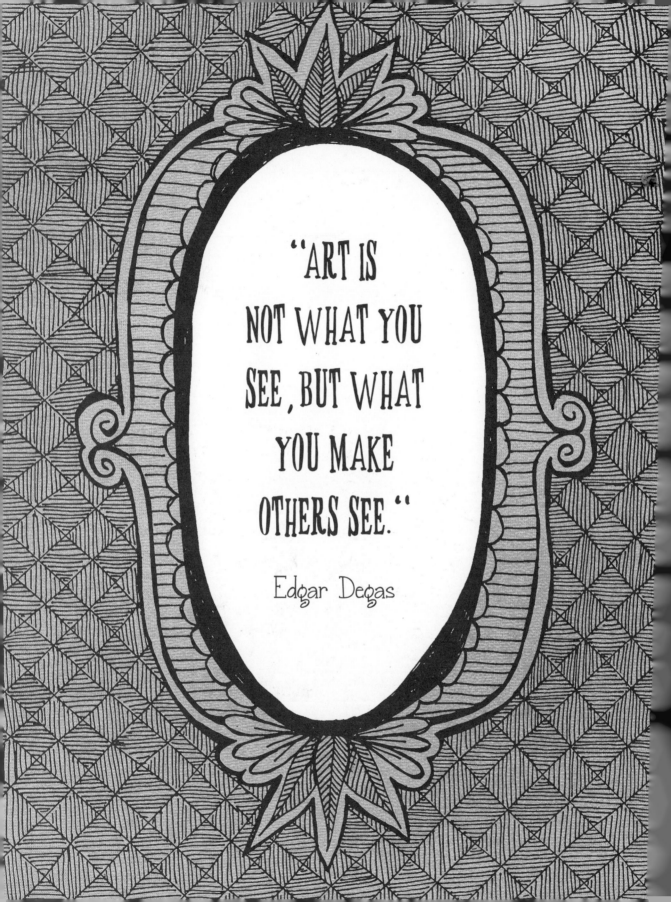